# This Book Belongs to

Publisher: W. Quay Hays

Art direction and illustration: Maritta Tapanainen

This book is dedicated to my daughter, Alice Coleman,
and to my Mom and Dad, Alice and Edward E. Coleman.

It is also dedicated to all of the people in my own Personal Memoir, including:
Ken Johnson, Mike Egan, Ken Medlock, Dana Johnson, Shecky Mulligan, Richard Antone,
George Tapps, Tom O'Reilly, Dean Barkley, Alan Krieger, Nick Mariano, Jack Scalia, Lillian Muller,
Mary Coleman Dybsky, Ann Coleman Campbell and Tom Coleman. I want to particularly thank
my brother Pat Coleman, my sister Margaret Coleman Gadient and Steve Gadient.

For information:
General Publishing Group, Inc.
2701 Ocean Park Boulevard, Suite 140
Santa Monica, CA 90405

Printed and bound in the USA by RR Donnelley & Sons Company
10 9 8 7 6 5 4 3 2 1

General Publishing Group
*Los Angeles*

# MY LIFE

## A
## PERSONAL
## MEMOIR

Created by John Coleman

GENERAL PUBLISHING GROUP
LOS ANGELES

# TABLE OF CONTENTS

# MY LIFE
## A PERSONAL MEMOIR

Memories are something special and beautiful to be enjoyed and appreciated over and over many times.

This book allows you to collect your most treasured memories and have an incredible life experience writing them down and recalling them.

Memories are something you can share with your loved ones; memories of your hopes and dreams, memories of your fears, victories and defeats. Some are funny, some are touching, some were painful and some still are. They all are you. When completed, this book can be kept next to the family photo album.

This treasure of memories can be enjoyed again and again.

# DIRECTIONS

Filling in your treasured memories will be both fun and challenging. It should be a joyful endeavor. You will be able to savor and enjoy the reliving of memories and gain a deeper understanding of who you are and what makes you tick.

There are, of course, many different ways to approach this personal memoir. First of all, it should not, and could not, be done in one day. I think you must go through it at least three times. Many things will be remembered later and added. I promise that when you have it half filled in and can't think of anything more to add, you will soon think of many more things and revisit the entries.

The idea is to list your most cherished memories. A word or phrase is enough. It is not necessary to use detailed explanations, as this is not a diary.

This personal inventory may well help your self-understanding and self-esteem, and it could be a very useful tool in your journey to your highest self.

Finally, remember to note the downside of the "good" and upside of the "bad."

Welcome to your treasure of memories!

The better part
of one's life
consists of his
friendships.

—*Abraham Lincoln*

# BEST FRIENDS

*People with whom you shared good times and bad,
laughs and tears, throughout the years.
Don't forget those with whom you are no longer in touch.*

1. _____
2. _____
3. _____
4. _____
5. _____
6. _____
7. _____
8. _____
9. _____
10. _____
11. _____
12. _____
13. _____
14. _____
15. _____
16. _____
17. _____
18. _____
19. _____
20. _____

Those who
bring sunshine
into the lives
of others
cannot keep it
from themselves.

# MOST INTERESTING PEOPLE I'VE MET

*This can even include people you did not like.*

1. _____

2. _____

3. _____

4. _____

5. _____

6. _____

7. _____

8. _____

9. _____

10. _____

11. _____

12. _____

13. _____

14. _____

15. _____

16. _____

17. _____

18. _____

19. _____

20. _____

Hold fast to dreams
for if dreams die,
life is a broken-
winged bird that
cannot fly.

—*Unknown*

# HEROES

*People who inspired you in one way or another.*
*Heroes come from all walks of life.*
*Some are in sports, some in education, some in music,*
*in theater or simply from the neighborhood.*

1. _____
2. _____
3. _____
4. _____
5. _____
6. _____
7. _____
8. _____
9. _____
10. _____
11. _____
12. _____
13. _____
14. _____
15. _____
16. _____
17. _____
18. _____
19. _____
20. _____

Humor is my sword
and my shield.
It protects me.
You can open a door
with humor and drive
a truck right through.

—*Alan Simpson*

# FUNNIEST STORIES FROM SCHOOL

*Ah, youth! Some of the greatest and some of the
toughest times in our lives were at school.*

1. _____
_____
_____
_____

2. _____
_____
_____
_____

3. _____
_____
_____
_____

4. _____
_____
_____
_____

5. _____
_____
_____
_____

Cherish yesterday...
Dream tomorrow...
*Live* today.

# BEST TIMES

*They still make you smile and feel good inside—
the greatest moments and periods in your life.*

1. _____
2. _____
3. _____
4. _____
5. _____
6. _____
7. _____
8. _____
9. _____
10. _____
11. _____
12. _____
13. _____
14. _____
15. _____
16. _____
17. _____
18. _____
19. _____
20. _____

# FOOTPRINTS

One night a man had a dream.
He dreamed he was walking along
the beach with the LORD. Across the sky
flashed scenes from his life. For each
scene, he noticed two sets of footprints
in the sand: one belonged to him,
and the other to the LORD.

When the last scene of his life flashed
before him, he looked back at the
footprints in the sand. He noticed that
many times along the path of his life
there was only one set of footprints.
He also noticed that it happened at the
very lowest and saddest times in his life.

This really bothered him and he
questioned the LORD about it. "LORD,
you said that once I decided to follow
you, you'd walk with me all the way.
But I have noticed that during the most
troublesome times in my life, there is
only one set of footprints. I don't
understand why, when I needed you
most you would leave me."

The LORD replied, "My precious,
precious child, I love you and I would
never leave you. During your times
of trial and suffering, when you see only
one set of footprints, it was then that
I carried you."

# WORST TIMES

*In retrospect, it's interesting: The bad times don't seem as bad…*
*They don't hurt anymore…Maybe you can even laugh!*

1. _____

_____

2. _____

_____

3. _____

_____

4. _____

_____

5. _____

_____

6. _____

_____

7. _____

_____

8. _____

_____

9. _____

_____

10. _____

_____

Live life
so you never
have to look back
and wish you'd
tried something.

# FAVORITE MOVIES

*Movies touch us, teach us, inspire us, make us laugh and make us cry.*
*What are some of the films that you will never forget?*

1. _____
2. _____
3. _____
4. _____
5. _____
6. _____
7. _____
8. _____
9. _____
10. _____
11. _____
12. _____
13. _____
14. _____
15. _____
16. _____
17. _____
18. _____
19. _____
20. _____

## An Irish Tribute

God Then Made Man,

The Italian for Music and Art,

The French for Fine Food,

The German for Intelligence,

The Swedes for Their Beauty,

The Jew for Religion,

And On and On Until

He Looked at What

He Had Created and Said,

"This Is All Very Fine but

No One Is Having Any Fun.

I Guess I'll Have To Make Me An

IRISHMAN."

# FAVORITE TV SHOWS

*List the most unforgettable episodes and series.*
*What do you watch today?*

1. _____
2. _____
3. _____
4. _____
5. _____
6. _____
7. _____
8. _____
9. _____
10. _____
11. _____
12. _____
13. _____
14. _____
15. _____
16. _____
17. _____
18. _____
19. _____
20. _____

The only true comment
on a piece of music
is another piece of music.

—*Igor Stravinsky*

# SONGS THAT MEAN SOMETHING TO ME

*Music touches times in our lives and chords in our hearts.*
*It's general and specific. It's wonderful.*

1. _____
2. _____
3. _____
4. _____
5. _____
6. _____
7. _____
8. _____
9. _____
10. _____
11. _____
12. _____
13. _____
14. _____
15. _____
16. _____
17. _____
18. _____
19. _____
20. _____

Turn your
stumbling blocks
into stepping
stones.

# BOOKS

*Which are your favorites and why? Is there one you always wanted
to read and are still curious about?
Did one or more dramatically affect your life?*

1. _____

2. _____

3. _____

4. _____

5. _____

6. _____

7. _____

8. _____

9. _____

10. _____

What hunger is
in relation to food,
zest is in relation
to life.

—Bertrand Russell

# FAVORITE FOODS

*Include meals, recipes, candy, appetizers,
breakfast, lunch, dinner and desserts.*

1. _____
_____

2. _____
_____

3. _____
_____

4. _____
_____

5. _____
_____

6. _____
_____

7. _____
_____

8. _____
_____

9. _____
_____

10. _____
_____

## LITTLE THINGS

Most of us
miss out
on life's
big prizes.
The Pulitzer.
The Nobel.
Oscars.
Tonys.
Emmys.
But we're
all eligible
for life's
small pleasures.
A pat
on the back.
A kiss
Behind the ear.
A four-pound bass.
A full moon.
An empty
parking space.
A crackling fire.
A great meal.
A glorious sunset.
Hot soup.
Cold beer.
Don't fret
about
copping life's
grand awards.
Enjoy its
tiny delights.
There are plenty
for all of us.

# WATER

*Favorite rivers, lakes or oceans.*

1. _____

2. _____

3. _____

4. _____

5. _____

6. _____

7. _____

8. _____

9. _____

10. _____

Life
only demands
from you
the strength
you possess.

—Dag Hammarskjöld

# MOST EMBARRASSING MOMENTS

*Yours, your friends', maybe some you've only heard or read about.*

1. _____

2. _____

3. _____

4. _____

5. _____

6. _____

7. _____

8. _____

9. _____

10. _____

When I have
listened
to my mistakes
I have grown.

—*Hugh Prather*

# REGRETS

*We've all had a few.*
*Sometimes they weren't so bad...sometimes they were.*

1. _____
_____

2. _____
_____

3. _____
_____

4. _____
_____

5. _____
_____

6. _____
_____

7. _____
_____

8. _____
_____

9. _____
_____

10. _____
_____

We all carry it within us;
supreme strength, the fullness
of wisdom, unquenchable joy.
It is never thwarted and cannot
be destroyed.

—*Hutsin Smith*

# LIVING PEOPLE WITH WHOM
## I'D LIKE TO DINE

*...or hang out, party, go to a ball game or a fight, see a movie, watch TV or vacation.*

1. _____

2. _____

3. _____

4. _____

5. _____

6. _____

7. _____

8. _____

9. _____

10. _____

11. _____

12. _____

13. _____

14. _____

15. _____

16. _____

17. _____

18. _____

19. _____

20. _____

A true friend
or
a good family
helps your health
as much as
a doctor.

# DEAD PEOPLE WITH WHOM I'D LIKE TO DINE

*Family, friends, notable historical figures.*

1. _____
2. _____
3. _____
4. _____
5. _____
6. _____
7. _____
8. _____
9. _____
10. _____
11. _____
12. _____
13. _____
14. _____
15. _____
16. _____
17. _____
18. _____
19. _____
20. _____

A man's
doubts
and fears
are his worst
enemy.

—*William Wrigley Jr.*

# BIGGEST FEARS

*From snakes to sharks to airplane crashes or fire,
what are yours?*

1. _____

2. _____

3. _____

4. _____

5. _____

6. _____

7. _____

8. _____

9. _____

10. _____

Sin your way
to happiness.

# FUNNIEST WORK STORIES

*For most, their jobs have elements of drudgery,*
*but some of the things that would be missed*
*if we didn't have to go to work are...*

1. _____

_____

_____

2. _____

_____

_____

3. _____

_____

_____

4. _____

_____

_____

5. _____

_____

_____

On the outside
one is a star.
But in reality,
one is
completely alone,
doubting everything.
To experience
this loneliness
of soul
is the hardest thing
in the world.

—Brigitte Bardot

# IF I COULD CHANGE PLACES WITH SOMEONE, WHO WOULD IT BE AND WHY?

1.

2.

3.

4.

5.

# Attitude is everything.

—*John Coleman*

# INCIDENTS THAT SHAPED
# MY PERSONALITY

*There are incidents in our lives that affect us so much we are never quite the same.*
*They may even send us down a different path in life.*

1. _____

_____

2. _____

_____

3. _____

_____

4. _____

_____

5. _____

_____

Dreams
come true...
if you make them.
You have to do
the work.

*—John Coleman*

# MY DREAMS

*Describe them in a little detail and note both
the upside and downside of achieving them.*

1. _____
_____
_____
_____

2. _____
_____
_____
_____

3. _____
_____
_____
_____

You have powers you
never dreamed of.
You can do things you
never thought you could do.
There are no limitations
in what you can do except
the limitations in your
own mind as to what
you cannot do.
Don't think you cannot.
Think you can.

—*Darwin P. Kingsley*

# HOW WOULD I LIKE TO BE DIFFERENT?

*Your personality, your physical attributes, job status,*
*place in life, health, family situation…*

1. _____
_____
_____

2. _____
_____
_____

3. _____
_____
_____

4. _____
_____
_____

5. _____
_____
_____

The best and
most beautiful
things in the world
cannot be seen
or even touched.
They must be felt
with the heart.

—*Helen Keller*

# DECISIONS THAT CHANGED MY LIFE

*What choices altered the path of your life, and why did you make them?*
*How did your life change?*

1. _____

_____

2. _____

_____

3. _____

_____

4. _____

_____

5. _____

_____

Pleasure
is the only thing
to live for.
Nothing ages
like happiness.

—Oscar Wilde

# PET PEEVES

*What really bugs you—anything and everything!*
*From personal things to politicians to cats…*

1. _____
2. _____
3. _____
4. _____
5. _____
6. _____
7. _____
8. _____
9. _____
10. _____
11. _____
12. _____
13. _____
14. _____
15. _____
16. _____
17. _____
18. _____
19. _____
20. _____

If I accept
the sunshine
and warmth,
I must also accept
the thunder
and the lightning.

—*Kahlil Gibran*

# THINGS I DIDN'T WANT TO DO...BUT DID

*They can change your life.*
*Did you meet a friend or lover, avoid an accident, bump into a job or career?*

1. _____

2. _____

3. _____

4. _____

5. _____

6. _____

7. _____

8. _____

9. _____

10. _____

# PRESS ON

NOTHING IN THE WORLD CAN TAKE
THE PLACE OF PERSISTENCE.

TALENT WILL NOT;
NOTHING IS MORE COMMON THAN
UNSUCCESSFUL MEN WITH TALENT.

GENIUS WILL NOT;
UNREWARDED GENIUS IS ALMOST A
PROVERB.

EDUCATION ALONE WILL NOT;
THE WORLD IS FULL OF EDUCATED
DERELICTS.

PERSISTENCE AND DETERMINATION
ALONE ARE OMNIPOTENT.

# BEST TEACHERS

*Teaching is the most important profession.*
*Include coaches and mentors.*

1. _____

   _____

   _____

2. _____

   _____

   _____

3. _____

   _____

   _____

4. _____

   _____

   _____

5. _____

   _____

   _____

On Life

What a wonderful life I've had!
I only wish I'd realized it sooner.

—*Colette*

# MENTORS

*If you are lucky enough to have had one or more,
you are an extremely fortunate person. How did they help?*

1. _____

_____

_____

2. _____

_____

_____

3. _____

_____

_____

4. _____

_____

_____

5. _____

_____

In all things of nature
there is something
marvelous.

—*Aristotle*

# BIGGEST INSECURITIES

*We all have our own flaws that trouble us.*
*Sometimes all it takes to accept them is to admit them!*

1.

2.

3.

4.

5.

The poor man
is not he who
is without a cent,
but he who
is without a dream.

—*Harry Kemp*

# FAVORITE PLACES

*List the most incredible spots you've ever visited or lived in,
or that have always intrigued you.*

1. _____

2. _____

3. _____

4. _____

5. _____

6. _____

7. _____

8. _____

9. _____

10. _____

"I love you!"

The three most important
and powerful words
in the world.

—*John Coleman*

# THINGS I WISH I'D SAID

*Maybe you were afraid, momentarily speechless or just wanted to avoid a fight.*
*Here you can say anything you want without any repercussions.*

1. _____

_____

_____

2. _____

_____

_____

3. _____

_____

_____

4. _____

_____

_____

5. _____

_____

_____

It takes a long time
to grow young.

—*Pablo Picasso*

# GUARDIAN ANGELS

*If you believe in angels, do you believe they can take human form?*
*Do angels help us in times of need (and hide their identity)?*
*When have angels helped you, your friends or your family?*

1. _____

_____

_____

_____

2. _____

_____

_____

_____

3. _____

_____

_____

_____

Do not wait for
ideal circumstances,
nor for the best opportunities;
they will never come.

—*Janet Erskine Stuart*

# THANK YOUS

*One last chance to say it.*
*Include the ones left unsaid!*

1. _____

   _____

2. _____

   _____

3. _____

   _____

4. _____

   _____

5. _____

   _____

6. _____

   _____

7. _____

   _____

8. _____

   _____

9. _____

   _____

10. _____

    _____

## LOVE

There is no difficulty that
enough love will not conquer;
No disease that enough love
will not heal;
No door that enough love
will not open;
No gulf that enough love
will not bridge;
No wall that enough love
will not throw down;
No sin that enough love
will not redeem...

It makes no difference how
deeply seated may be the trouble;
How hopeless the outlook;
How muddled the tangle;
How great the mistake.
A sufficient realization of love
will dissolve it all...
If only you could love enough
you would be the happiest and
most powerful being in the world.

—*Emmet Fox*

# IF I HAD KNOWN THEN...

*...what I know now.*
*Things you would have done differently,*
*but you didn't know better at the time...*

1. _____
   _____

2. _____
   _____

3. _____
   _____

4. _____
   _____

5. _____
   _____

6. _____
   _____

7. _____
   _____

8. _____
   _____

9. _____
   _____

10. _____
    _____

Three things in human life
are important.
The first is to be kind.
The second is to be kind.
The third is to be kind.

—Henry James

# GOOD DEEDS

*The ways you've helped others.*
*Be proud of yourself and do some more.*

1. _____

_____

2. _____

_____

3. _____

_____

4. _____

_____

5. _____

_____

6. _____

_____

7. _____

_____

8. _____

_____

9. _____

_____

10. _____

_____

To the person with a toothache, even if the world is tottering, there is nothing more important than a visit to the dentist.

—*George Bernard Shaw*

# BEST FEATURES

*Physical and other.*

1. _____

   _____

   _____

2. _____

   _____

   _____

3. _____

   _____

   _____

4. _____

   _____

   _____

5. _____

   _____

   _____

There are no victims
— only volunteers.

—*Billi Gordon*

# BIGGEST FAULTS

*We all have them. What are yours?*

1. _____

   _____

   _____

2. _____

   _____

   _____

3. _____

   _____

   _____

4. _____

   _____

   _____

5. _____

   _____

   _____

I'm tired of
all this nonsense
about beauty being
only skin deep.
That's deep enough.
What do you want — an
adorable pancreas?

—*Jean Kerr*

# PHYSICAL FLAWS

*Did you know that everyone else has them, too?*
*Some people don't like their own hair. Many don't like their height.*
*You don't like…*

1. _____

_____

_____

2. _____

_____

_____

3. _____

_____

_____

4. _____

_____

_____

5. _____

_____

_____

Passion—
There simply
can be nothing more.
There simply
should be nothing less.

—*Jeanne (Jhett) Jensen*

# THINGS TO DO

*List your top 20.*

1. _____
2. _____
3. _____
4. _____
5. _____
6. _____
7. _____
8. _____
9. _____
10. _____
11. _____
12. _____
13. _____
14. _____
15. _____
16. _____
17. _____
18. _____
19. _____
20. _____

Take time to work—
it is the price of success.
Take time to think—
it is the source of power.
Take time to play—
it is the secret of perpetual youth.
Take time to read—
it is the foundation of wisdom.
Take time to be friendly—
it is the road to happiness.
Take time to dream—
it is hitching your wagon to a star.
Take time to love and be loved—
it is the privilege of the Gods.
Take time to look around—
the day is too short to be selfish.
Take time to laugh—
it is the music of the soul.

*—An Old Irish Prayer*

# TEN TIMES I'VE CRIED

*Movies, onions, frustrations, childhood bumps...*
*and other big hurts or sadnesses.*

1. 

2. 

3. 

4. 

5. 

6. 

7. 

8. 

9. 

10.

A graceful and
honorable old age
is the childhood
of immortality.

—*Pindar*

# WHAT'S KEEPING ME FROM ACHIEVING WHAT I WANT?

1. _____

_____

_____

_____

2. _____

_____

_____

_____

3. _____

_____

_____

_____

4. _____

_____

_____

_____

5. _____

_____

_____

_____

A light heart lives long.

—*William Shakespeare*

# PLEDGES TO MYSELF

*Many people want to lose weight but few keep it off.*
*Before my life is over, I promise to...*

1. _____

_____

_____

2. _____

_____

_____

3. _____

_____

_____

4. _____

_____

_____

5. _____

_____

_____

Perfection does not exist.
To understand this
is the triumph
of human intelligence;
to expect to possess it
is the most dangerous
kind of madness.

—*Alfred de Raisset*

# FAVORITE VACATIONS

*Where? When? With whom?*
*What's your favorite memory?*

1. _____
_____

2. _____
_____

3. _____
_____

4. _____
_____

5. _____
_____

6. _____
_____

7. _____
_____

8. _____
_____

9. _____
_____

10. _____
_____

It is a very funny thing
about life:
if you refuse to accept
anything but the best
you very often get it.

—W. Somerset Maugham

# TRIPS TO TAKE

*Where? Why? With whom? When?*

1.

2.

3.

4.

5.

6.

7.

8.

9.

10.

I will make
this day
a happy one,
for I alone
can determine
what kind of day
it will be.

# BEST PRACTICAL JOKES

*That you played, were played on you or you witnessed
at your school, work or in your neighborhood.*

1. _____
   _____

2. _____
   _____

3. _____
   _____

4. _____
   _____

5. _____
   _____

6. _____
   _____

7. _____
   _____

8. _____
   _____

9. _____
   _____

10. _____
    _____

Do not stand at my grave and weep,
I am not there, I do not sleep.
I am a thousand winds that blow,
I am the diamond glints on snow.
I am the sunlight on ripened grain;
I am the gentle autumn's rain.
When you awaken in the morning's hush,
I am the swift uplifting rush
Of quiet birds in circled flight.
I am the soft star that shines at night.
Do not stand at my grave and cry.
I am not there; I did not die.

*—Unknown*

# ONE YEAR TILL PAINLESS DEATH

*If death was painless, and you knew it would be peaceful, would you still fear it?*
*What would you say, do, feel in the meantime?*

1. _____

_____

2. _____

_____

3. _____

_____

4. _____

_____

5. _____

_____

6. _____

_____

7. _____

_____

8. _____

_____

9. _____

_____

10. _____

_____

The secret
of staying young
is to live honestly,
eat slowly,
and lie about
your age.

—*Lucille Ball*

# THREE WISHES

*If you had Aladdin's lamp, what would they be?*
*Rub away…*

1. _____
   _____
   _____
   _____

2. _____
   _____
   _____
   _____

3. _____
   _____
   _____
   _____

It's pretty hard
to tell what does
bring happiness;
poverty and wealth
have both failed.

—Kim Hubbard

# MONEY

*What victories and defeats have you known in the game of money?*

1. _____

_____

_____

2. _____

_____

_____

3. _____

_____

_____

4. _____

_____

_____

5. _____

_____

No girl, however
intelligent and warmhearted,
can possibly know or feel
half as much at 20
as she will at 35.

—Stephen Vizinczey

# ADVENTURES

*What are the wildest things you ever did?*
*What are the craziest things you want to do?*

1. _____

   _____

2. _____

   _____

3. _____

   _____

4. _____

   _____

5. _____

   _____

6. _____

   _____

7. _____

   _____

8. _____

   _____

9. _____

   _____

10. _____

    _____

If you can dream it
you can do it.

—*Bud Greenspan*

# PERSONAL ACCOMPLISHMENTS

*Your proudest moments and best deeds.*
*Even if they seemed small at the time, how did they help?*

1.

2.

3.

4.

5.

If we'd only stop trying
to be happy, we'd have
a pretty good time.

—*Edith Wharton*

# BIGGEST LESSONS LEARNED

*The most important truths you have come
to know in your lifetime.*

1. _____

2. _____

3. _____

4. _____

5. _____

6. _____

7. _____

8. _____

9. _____

10. _____

Unless each day
can be looked back upon
by an individual as one
in which he has some fun,
some joy, some real
satisfaction,
that day is a loss.

—*Dwight D. Eisenhower*

# CONCERTS, PLAYS, PERFORMANCES

*Live events can be incredibly thrilling and remembered for a lifetime.*

1. _____

2. _____

3. _____

4. _____

5. _____

6. _____

7. _____

8. _____

9. _____

10. _____

Enjoy the little things,
for one day you may
look back and realize
they were the big things.

—Robert Brault

# FAVORITE PETS

*Animals often become a treasured family member and enrich our lives.*

1.

2.

3.

4.

5.

Forgive all who
have offended you,
not for them,
but for yourself.

—*Harriet Utz Nelson*

# BIGGEST FIGHTS AND QUARRELS

*Our relationships can be heart-wrenching or funny. We may want to forget
the rancorous times but sometimes we carry them around for too long.
Get them out of the way.*

1.

2.

3.

4.

5.

If you want others
to be happy,
practice compassion.
If you want to be happy,
practice compassion.

—*Unknown*

# MEMORABLE NEIGHBORS

*They can either make life easier or more enjoyable.*
*Or they can make it rougher and be a huge problem.*

1.

2.

3.

4.

5.

Happiness is to be found
along the way,
not at the end of the road,
for then the journey
is over and it is too late.

—*Robert R. Updegraff*

# PARTIES AND CELEBRATIONS

*Times spent celebrating with others are often the most anticipated and fun occasions in our lives.*

1.

2.

3.

4.

5.

6.

7.

8.

9.

10.

If you survive long enough, you're revered—rather like an old building.

—*Katharine Hepburn*

# MOST MEMORABLE PROJECTS

*As a child or an adult; in school or at work—*
*What have been your most memorable hobbies or undertakings?*

1.

2.

3.

4.

5.

6.

7.

8.

9.

10.

Get action.
Do things; don't fritter
away your time.
Take a place wherever
you are and
be somebody.

—*Theodore Roosevelt*

# FAVORITE JOBS

*We've all probably held more than a few. Which ones did you love and which ones did you loathe?*

1. _____

_____

_____

2. _____

_____

_____

3. _____

_____

_____

4. _____

_____

_____

5. _____

_____

_____

To forgive is the highest, most beautiful form of love. In return you will receive untold peace and happiness.

—Robert Muller

# MOST INFURIATING PEOPLE

*Some people are so irritating that they leave you speechless.*
*Who pushed your buttons?*

1. _____

2. _____

3. _____

4. _____

5. _____

6. _____

7. _____

8. _____

9. _____

10. _____

# More than enough is too much.

— *Unknown*

# HOLIDAYS

*Too much partying, too much family, but moments you will never forget.*

1. _____
   _____
   _____

2. _____
   _____
   _____

3. _____
   _____
   _____

4. _____
   _____
   _____

5. _____
   _____

Unhappy is the man
whom man can
make unhappy.

—*Ralph Waldo Emerson*

# FAVORITE (AND NOT-SO-FAVORITE) SPORTS HEROES

*Who were the ones you rooted for and who were the ones you hated?*

1. _____

2. _____

3. _____

4. _____

5. _____

6. _____

7. _____

8. _____

9. _____

10. _____

There are risks and costs
to a program of action,
but they are less
than the long-range risks
and costs of comfortable
inaction.

—*John F. Kennedy*

# TIME CAPSULE

*If you could put things away for future generations,
what would they be and why?*

1. _____

_____

2. _____

_____

3. _____

_____

4. _____

_____

5. _____

_____

6. _____

_____

7. _____

_____

8. _____

_____

9. _____

_____

10. _____

When I was about eight,
I decided that the most
wonderful thing,
next to a human being,
was a book.

—Margaret Walker

# WRITERS

*Poets, songwriters, newspaper columnists, and authors.*
*Who taught you a new way to look at things or simply captured your heart?*

1. _____

2. _____

3. _____

4. _____

5. _____

6. _____

7. _____

8. _____

9. _____

10. _____

In search of my
mother's garden
I found my own.

—Alice Walker

# FLOWERS, PLANTS AND TREES

*The simple and often majestic qualities of these wonderful creations:*
*the beauty of the gladiola, the essence of jasmine, and the shade of the elm.*

1. _____

2. _____

3. _____

4. _____

5. _____

6. _____

7. _____

8. _____

9. _____

10. _____

My favorite thing is to go
where I've never been.

—*Diane Arbus*

# SECRET PLACES

*Where have you gone for solitude, peace and quiet?*

1. _____
   _____
   _____

2. _____
   _____
   _____

3. _____
   _____
   _____

4. _____
   _____
   _____

5. _____
   _____

Only the upright heart
that has its own logic and
its own reason is free.

—*Marc Chagall*

# ADVICE

*What are some of the most rewarding words of encouragement you have heard?*
*Who said them?*

1. _____

   _____

   _____

2. _____

   _____

   _____

3. _____

   _____

   _____

4. _____

   _____

   _____

5. _____

   _____

The great thing about getting older is that you don't lose all the other ages you've been.

—Madeleine L'Engle

# GAMES

*What are the games you loved as a child?*
*Which ones do you play now?*

1. _____

_____

_____

_____

2. _____

_____

_____

_____

3. _____

_____

_____

_____

Being independent,
answering to no one
and doing whatever
you want is one
of the two greatest
things in life.

The greatest is
sharing love.

—John Coleman

# DARKEST HOURS

*What were the lowest times of your life and how did you get through them?*

1. _____
   _____
   _____

2. _____
   _____
   _____

3. _____
   _____
   _____

4. _____
   _____

5. _____
   _____

A sense of humor
can help you
overlook
the unattractive,
tolerate
the unpleasant,
cope with
the unexpected,
and smile
through
the unbearable.

—Moshe Waldoks

# FAVORITE JOKES

*It is said that "laughter is the best medicine."*
*So what are the jokes that made you laugh?*

1. _____

_____

_____

_____

2. _____

_____

_____

_____

3. _____

_____

_____

_____

4. _____

_____

_____

5. _____

_____

_____

_____

I have no regrets.
I wouldn't have lived
my life the way
I did if I was going
to worry about
what people were
going to say.

—Ingrid Bergman

# WHAT DO YOU BELIEVE ABOUT SPIRITUALITY, GOD AND LIFE AFTER DEATH?

1.

2.

3.

4.

5.

On Laughter.
He who laughs, lasts.

—*Mary Pettibone Poole*

# BIGGEST CHANGES IN THE WORLD
## IN YOUR LIFETIME

1. _____

_____

_____

2. _____

_____

_____

3. _____

_____

_____

4. _____

_____

_____

5. _____

_____

I wish it were OK
in this country to look
one's age, whatever it is.
Maturity has a lot going for it,
even in terms of aesthetics.
For example, you no longer
get bubblegum stuck
in your braces.

—*Cyra McFadden*

# FAVORITE ARTWORK

*Any image you treasure (even your own or your childrens'!)...*

1. _____

_____

_____

2. _____

_____

_____

3. _____

_____

_____

4. _____

_____

_____

5. _____

_____

_____

Tell me what
you eat
and I will tell you
what you are.

—*Anthelme Brillat-Savarin*

# FAVORITE PHOTOS OF MYSELF

*Admit it. No false modesty. Paste them below.*

1.

2.

Never fear
that your life
might come
to an end;

Rather, fear
that it should
never begin.

# FUNERAL PLAN

*How would you like to be remembered?*
*If your funeral went exactly as you wished, how would it be?*
*Don't be afraid to use humor—jokes, remembrances, testimonials—and break traditions.*
*Who would speak?*

1. _____

_____

_____

_____

2. _____

_____

_____

_____

3. _____

_____

_____

_____

4. _____

_____

_____

5. _____

_____

_____

Let me observe,
with new interest,
even the commonplace
things that happen
in each new day.

—*Unknown*

# PRIZED POSSESSIONS

*Favorite souvenirs, mementos and items that have
a priceless value in your heart.*

1.

2.

3.

4.

5.

6.

7.

8.

9.

10.

Great-great-
grandfather

Great-great-
grandmother

Great-great-
grandmother

Great-great-
grandfather

Great-great-
grandfather

Great-great-
grandmother

Great-great-
grandmother

Great-great-
grandfather

Great-grandfather

Great-grandmother

Great-grandfather

Great-grandmother

Grandmother

Grandfather

Aunts and Uncles

Mother

Nieces and Nephews

Sisters and Brothers

# FAMILY TREE

Everyone's family is different,
so feel free to define your own family
by adding whatever branches you need.

Great-great-
grandfather

Great-great-
grandmother

Great-great-
grandmother

Great-great-
grandfather

Great-great-
grandfather

Great-great-
grandmother

Great-great-
grandmother

Great-great-
grandfather

Great-grandmother

Great-grandfather

Great-grandmother

Great-grandfather

Grandfather

Grandmother

Aunts and Uncles

Father

Children

Me

Spouse

NOTES

NOTES

NOTES